SPACE ENCYCLOPEDIA

OUR UNIVERSE

Om
KIDZ
An imprint of Om Books International

Contents

OUR UNIVERSE

▲ *Interestingly, for the first 380,000 years or even more, the universe was extremely hot for light to shine.*

The night sky has trillions and trillions of stars. Many of these are visible to the naked eye on a clear night. We can also see some of the planets that orbit our Sun, as well as the moon. All these objects are a part of our universe.

However, they aren't the only part of our universe. The stars and planets that we can detect are only a tiny part of everything that's out there. The observable universe is a sphere that is a little over 90 billion light years in diameter. The rest of it is invisible to us because the originating light, post the Big Bang, hasn't even reached us yet.

The Big Bang

The Big Bang Theory is a widely accepted explanation for the existence of our universe. It states that the universe began as a singularity from a hot, dense state and rapidly expanded (not exploded as the name suggests) over nearly 13.8 billion years to the state that we are in at present, and continues to expand. This model was proposed by Russian mathematician Alexander Friedmann and Belgian astronomer Georges Lemaître during the 1920s.

An infographic explaining the Big Bang and the following events:

Expanding and cooling universe

9 billion years later
Formation of the solar system and Earth.

300 million years later
Stars and galaxies begin to form.

380,000 years later
Electrons and nuclei combined into atoms.

First seconds after Big Bang
Birth of subatomic particles.

Approximately 13.8 billion years ago
Big Bang

Beginning of time and the dawn of light

According to this theory, the universe expanded from a highly compressed state (extremely high temperature and density). The cosmos contained a multitude of fundamental particles, such as electrons, neutrons and so on. The free electrons made it impossible for any light to pass through, thus rendering our universe in darkness. There was also a huge amount of dark energy, a mysterious force that is thought to be the driving force behind our universe's current acceleration.

Falling temperatures and the afterglow

As the universe expanded, it also began to cool down rapidly. The temperature dropped drastically from an extremely hot 5.5 billion degrees. This caused the elementary particles to combine or degrade. Specifically, the protons decayed and the free electrons combined with the nuclei. A million years later, this light started passing through the universe. This primary light, or the "afterglow", is known as the Cosmic Microwave Background Radiation (CMBR).

An artist's rendition of the afterglow of the bang starting to leak into the universe.

FUN FACT

American physicists Arno Penzias and Robert Wilson discovered the Cosmic Microwave Background Radiation quite accidentally in 1965. Along with evidence and fact, the scientists haven't yet been able to find any objects pre-dating the Big Bang. Hence, this theory has been accepted only as of now.

Before the Big Bang

The question of what the beginning of the universe was like has been debated and pondered for over millennia. Today, it is widely accepted that the universe began at some point—it hadn't always been this way. This brings us to an even more important question; what existed before it?

Supernatural theories

Many attribute the creation of the universe to a supernatural being, that is a God or several Gods. It is stated that in the beginning, the only entity that existed was "The Being". The rest of the creation was a void. And then, "The Being" brought the entire universe into existence.

The scientific perspective

Modern scientists mostly agree that the universe began around 14 billion years ago with the Big Bang. What preceded the Big Bang is hotly argued amongst the scientists. Until the twentieth century, most scientists did not even agree that the universe had a beginning, so this debate is a fairly recent one.

However, all scientists agree upon one thing that existed before the universe began: chaos, or rather, statistical chaos. This is a scientific way of saying that we have no way of knowing for certain. All the laws of physics that hold true now and have held true since the last 14 billion years would have broken down at this beginning.

The bigger picture

One of the most popular theories is that our universe is a child universe, that our universe broke away from a parent universe during the Big Bang. If you consider the universe to consist of everything, it's difficult to understand how it could have come from something even bigger. If our planet is a part of a solar system, which is a part of a galaxy, which is a part of a universe, which is a part of a parent universe, can you imagine how vast infinity is?

However, the idea of something existing "before" the Big Bang is flawed. Before the Big Bang, the concept of time didn't exist. Therefore, the idea of something coming "before" couldn't exist either.

▶ *The birth of the universe was as a flash of light breaking through. Pictured here is an artist's imagination of this beginning.*

Other Theories of our Universe

The Big Bang is the most popular theory in existence today. However, there are and probably always will be other theories competing with this one. Some of the originally proposed theories have already been discarded. A theory is discarded if what has been observed of the universe does not match the predictions of the said theory.

Some of the more common theories are explained below:

Oscillation Model Theory – It states that the universe is a cyclic process.

Steady State Theory – Here, it is believed that the universe has no beginning or end. Matter is being continuously created. The theory is not prevalent at the moment.

Hawking–Turok Theory – This theory states that the universe was instantaneously created from a tiny particle like a pea. What this particle was made from is yet to be explored, but that is how it began.

Eternal Inflation Theory – The assumption here is that there are an infinite number of universes. Our universe is just one among them. There was a rapid expansion following the Big Bang. According to this theory, the rapid expansion never really stopped. It just continued in other universes. Thus, this inflation is "eternal".

Oscillation Model Theory

This theorises that the universe is a cyclic process. It started with a Big Bang and will continue till the universe expands to its maximum size. At this point, there will be a rapid contraction, called the "big crunch", until the universe contracts back to a single point. This singularity would then explode again, restarting the cycle. These oscillating cycles are a result of the collision of "branes". The branes are thought of as multi-dimensional membranes with something called a higher-dimensional volume. The mathematical model for these is quite complex.

▲ *An artist's rendering of an oscillating universe.*

The Steady State Theory

This theory is now an obsolete, expanding universe model. It was proposed as an alternative to the Big Bang theory. In this theory, new matter is continuously created as the universe expands.

Majority of cosmologists, astrophysicists and astronomers now reject this theory. The observational evidence points to a cosmology with a finite age of the universe. This theory does not predict any age or a distinct point of origin. The idea was originally proposed by Sir James Jeans during the 1920s.

▶ *Sir James Jeans.*

FUN FACT

Among the varied theories about the universe, one states that the universe is nothing but a hologram. It's a flat, two-dimensional image that is projected onto a sphere by a vast computer.

This theory asserts that although the universe is expanding, it does not change its appearance over time; therefore, the universe has no beginning or end.

Steven Weinberg explained its failure as, "The steady state model does not appear to agree with the observed dL versus z relation or with the source counts... In a sense, the disagreement is a credit to the model. Alone among all cosmologies, the steady-state model makes such definite predictions that it can be disproved even with the limited observational evidence at our disposal". Thus, it was credited as a good example of cosmic theory, although it is incorrect.

Neil Turok and Stephen Hawking, authors of the Hawking–Turok theory

Eternal Inflation Theory

Our universe is just one among the many universes that exist. According to this theory, the rapid expansion, following the Big Bang, never really stopped. It just continued in other universes. Thus, this inflation is "eternal". In theories of eternal inflation, the phase of the inflation of our universe's expansion will never end. This is true for only some regions of our universe. As these regions expand very quickly, most of the volume of our universe at any given time is inflating.

▲ *This image is an artist's rendering of what different universes being born rapidly would look like. This collection of multiple universes is known as a multiverse.*

The Hawking–Turok Theory

This theory co-exists with the Big Bang. Rather than explaining the Big Bang itself, it tries to explain that the Big Bang needed an impetus. This impetus was provided by a particle that they describe as an "instanton". The instanton is a hypothetical particle that has the mass of a pea but is much, much smaller in size. As a result of this basic assumption, the theory is also called the "universe from a pea" theory.

▲ *This cone is supposed to represent the space-time continuum. The direction of the arrow shows how it progresses. It starts as time moves up along the height of the cone while space moves around the width of the cone. The continuum is then a cone with its tip pointing downwards. As a result, at the tip, both space and time meet at a single point. This point is known as the "singularity".*

Wormholes

A wormhole is a passage through the space-time continuum that could create a quicker route for long journeys across the universe. This is true only in theory. The existence of wormholes is predicted on the basis of the theory of general relativity. They could be dangerous and in case of a sudden collapse, extreme radiation and unsafe contact with exotic matter could occur.

Wormholes and the theory of general relativity

Lorentzian wormholes, also known as "Schwarzschild wormholes" or "Einstein–Rosen bridges" connect the spaces that can be modelled as vacuum resolutions of Einstein's field equations, through merging models of black and white holes. Physicists Albert Einstein and Nathan Rosen used the theory of general relativity in 1935 to suggest that "bridges" may exist that connect two different points in space and time, creating a shortcut, reducing the travelling time and distance, but only in theory.

What do wormholes look like?

They have two, possibly spheroidal, mouths that are connected by a throat, which could be straight or winding. Astrophysicist Stephen Hawking suggests that wormholes may exist in "quantum foam", the smallest environment in the universe, where extremely small tunnels continuously open and close, temporarily connecting different places and time.

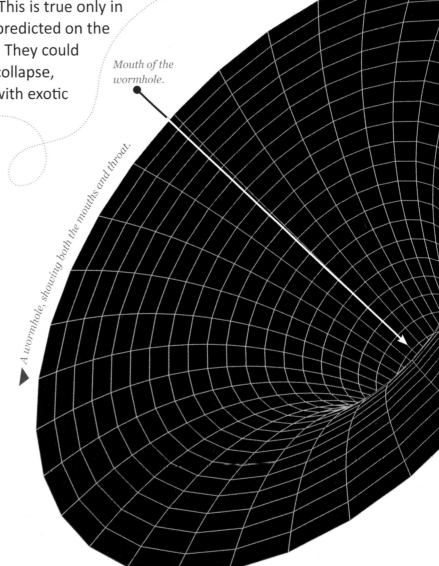

Mouth of the wormhole.

A wormhole, showing both the mouths and throat.

Problems of wormholes

Size: It is predicted that ancient wormholes exist on microscopic levels, which are about 10^{-33} cm wide. However, with the expansion of the universe, there is a possibility that some may have stretched to larger sizes.

Stability: The Einstein–Rosen wormholes would not be helpful for travel because they collapse quickly. However, recent research suggests that a wormhole containing "exotic" matter could remain open and unchanged for longer periods.

Exotic matter: Exotic matter contains negative energy density and huge negative pressure. If a wormhole contained adequate exotic matter, it could be used as a means of sending information or travellers through space.

FUN FACT

Wormholes are so tiny that humans couldn't use them, but with new technologies, scientists could possibly capture and enlarge them so that they could be useful to us.

Abstract teleportation in the wormhole.

Time travel

Besides connecting two separate regions within the universe, a wormhole could also connect two different universes. Some scientists speculate that if one mouth of a wormhole is positioned in a certain manner, time travel would become possible. However, Stephen Hawking argued against this. Though adding exotic matter to a wormhole may stabilise it to the extent that humans could travel safely through it, there is a possibility that the addition of "regular" matter could destabilise it as well.

Throat of the wormhole.

Too small for time travel

Wormholes such as these might prove to be too small and brief for human time travel. The question being, would we one day learn how to capture, stabilise and broaden them? According to Hawking, this is surely possible as long as we prepare ourselves for some feedback. If we were to artificially extend the life of a tunnel through folded space-time, then there is a possibility that a radiation feedback loop may occur; this would destroy the time tunnel like an audio feedback can ruin a speaker.

A tunnel in space

In space, when masses put pressure on different regions of the universe they could finally come together to form a type of tunnel. Theoretically, the so called tunnel would then, join two separate times and allow passage between them. It is also possible that some sudden physical or quantum property could avert such a wormhole from occurring.

Speedy travel

Wormholes allow superluminal or faster-than-light travel by ensuring that the speed of light is not exceeded locally at any time. While travelling through a wormhole, subluminal or slower-than-light speeds are used. If two points are connected by a wormhole, then the time taken to cross it would be less than the time taken by a light beam to travel through space outside the wormhole. However, a light beam travelling through the wormhole would always be faster than the traveller. To understand this phenomenon better, we can use the analogy that running from one place to another may take longer than driving the same distance.

Mouth of the wormhole.

Will the Universe End?

There are several theories that predict the end of the universe. However, if it will actually occur is uncertain. Scientists have been researching this and have come up with three theories as to how our universe could come to an end. There are three schools of thought that consider the universe to be open, flat or closed.

Open universe

Studies suggest that the universe will expand forever. As it expands, the matter it contains will spread and become thinner and thinner. The galaxies will exhaust their resources to make new stars. The existing stars will slowly fade. Instead of a fiery structure, the galaxies will transform into coffins filled with dust and dead stars. Then, the universe will become dark, cold and eventually, lifeless.

Flat universe

In this scenario, the universe will consume all the energy from the Big Bang and after it has consumed all the energy, thereby exhausting it, the universe will come to a stop. This is a contrast to the open universe theory because it will take an infinite amount of time for the universe to reach the equilibrium point of the consumption of energy.

Closed universe

Astronomers believe that a closed universe will reduce its pace until it reaches its maximum size. Then, it will recoil, collapsing on itself. Simultaneously, the universe will become denser and hotter until it ends in a hot and dense singularity. A closed universe will lead to what is called a "big crunch", which is the opposite of the Big Bang. However, scientists are still researching the end of our universe.

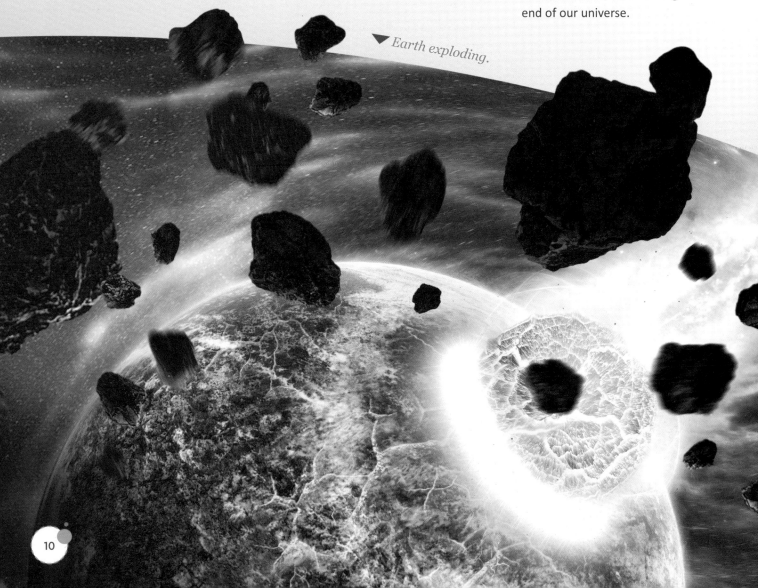

▼ *Earth exploding.*

A multiverse is a portmanteau of the words "multiple" and "universe".

The big crunch

This is based on Einstein's theory of general relativity. This theory suggests that the universe's expansion will stop at a certain point and it will begin to collapse into itself, pulling everything with it until it is transformed into the biggest black hole.

To predict with certainty the possibility of a big crunch, scientists must first determine definite properties of the universe, such as density. They believe that if density is larger than a particular value called 'critical density', a final collapse is possible.

Multiverse

The multiverse theory states that there will be no real end to the universe. It states that when our universe was created, there were multiple more universes created and that they are all at different stages of their existence. When our universe ends, there will be other universes that will still go on and newer universes that will be created.

False vacuum

A false vacuum is a vacuum where the entropy is great but has not yet reached its maximum state. As a result, there is still a lower energy state that can be reached and some usable energy left in this false vacuum. This theory believes that every time we reach such a false vacuum, the universe decays to reach a true vacuum and begins multiple new universes in the process.

The big bounce

This is a theorised scientific model related to the beginning of the known universe. According to one version of the Big Bang theory of cosmology, in the beginning, the universe had infinite density. This seems to be at odds with everything else in physics. The big bounce is also a cyclic theory. It consists of multiple repetitions of the Big Bang followed by big crunches. The main difference is the absence of the "brane membranes" that dilate and bleed entropy out of the universe.

Our Universe Today

Our universe is huge and includes those things that we can see and know about, as well as those that we cannot. The planets, stars and galaxies comprise only a small part of it. The part of the universe that we can see is called the observable universe. It is currently about 91 billion light years in diameter. The size of the entire universe is unknown and may be infinite. There are probably more than a 100 billion galaxies in the observable universe. Currently, our universe is made up of the following elements:

Energetic universe

There is a lot of energy in our universe. This energy might help explain the mystery of its infiniteness. There are both positive and negative energies present. However, light energy allows us to see the objects in our universe. The energy present in celestial objects helps us to get a better understanding of it. Another form of energy that exists in the universe is that of the X-rays.

Distant quasar

Quasars are extremely bright centres of distant galaxies powered by supermassive black holes at their centres. Their light may help us probe the period when the first stars and galaxies were forming. Quasars are studied through telescopes both on Earth and in space.

◀ An x-ray image of NGC 4258/M106, a galaxy with extra arms, a supermassive black hole and a light illustration of glowing gas.

Galaxy group

Studies suggest that galaxies exist in groups. Galaxies that are a part of such groups frequently interact and even merge together in a vibrant cosmic merging of interacting gravity.

Star cluster

When the stars are born, they grow from large clouds of gas. As a result, they form in groups or clusters. After the remnant gas is heated and blown away, the stars come together due to gravity.

Star birth

Stars are born when clouds of gases and dust collapse. Due to this, their density and temperature increases. The temperature and density are highest at the centre of the cloud, where a new star eventually develops. The object that is formed at the centre of a collapsing cloud and which later grows into a star is called a "protostar".

Planet

Planets form one aspect of our universe. Our solar system has eight planets along with their natural satellites. The eight planets orbit the Sun. Interestingly, evidence shows that there are several other planets in other galaxies.

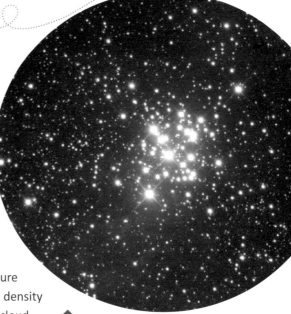

The Jewel box is a star cluster in our universe.

Small world

Besides the galaxies, stars and planets, there also exist objects that float around in space. These objects include comets, asteroids, meteors as well as moons of other planets.

Unknown universe

Scientists suggest that our universe is composed as follows: Approximately 68 per cent dark energy, 27 per cent dark matter and 5 per cent normal matter. Studies about dark energy continue to astonish scientists as very little is known about this energy.

Meteorites

Meteorites are fragments of rock and/or metal that fall from space to Earth. Meteorites break away from large extraterrestrial bodies. They can measure anything from a fraction of a millimetre to the size of a football pitch and bigger. When meteorites are caught by Earth's gravity, they move towards the planet at accelerated speeds of over 11.2 km per second. As they enter Earth's thick atmosphere, they rapidly slow down due to the friction and glow, moving across the sky like a flash of light, before finally crashing to the ground.

View of the planet Earth from space during a meteorite impact.

Where are meteorites found?

Many meteorites floating in space plunge towards the Earth's surface. Most of them fall into the sea. However, thousands of new meteorites are found each year. Meteorites can be found all over the world, but are easiest to spot in dry places, such as deserts, where they do not erode quickly and are less likely to be hidden by vegetation.

Where do they come from?

Some meteorites are fragments that have broken away during the collision of asteroids. Asteroids are irregular-shaped rocks that orbit the Sun. There are thousands of asteroids in our solar system, mostly located in an orbit between Mars and Jupiter, known as the asteroid belt. A small proportion of meteorites come from the moon and the planet Mars. These meteorites are much younger than those from asteroids, some as young as 2,500 million and 180 million years old, respectively.

Space rocks on Earth

At 60 tonnes, the Hoba meteorite found at Namibia is the heaviest meteorite rock to have been found by humans. It is estimated that it had fallen to Earth as recent as 800,000 years ago. Since it is flat, it is said that when it did fall to Earth, it skipped across the surface, much like a stone skipping across water.

Iron meteorite Gibeon from Namibia. ▼

Hoba meteorite - the largest meteorite ever found. ▼

Meteoroids and Meteors

A meteoroid is a small piece of rock, dust or metal travelling through space. They are significantly smaller than asteroids and range in size from small grains to one-metre wide objects.

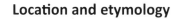

A meteorite trail near Chelyabinsk, Russia.

Space dust

Objects that are smaller than 1 m are classified as micrometeoroids or space dust. Some meteoroids may be fragments of comets or asteroids orbiting the Sun. Others are the result of debris ejected because of impacts on the Moon or even Mars.

Shooting stars

A meteor or a "shooting star" is the passage of a meteoroid or micrometeoroid into Earth's atmosphere. Here, it becomes incandescent from air friction and starts shedding glowing material in its wake. This is sufficient to create a visible streak of light.

▼ *A star trail image of meteors during meteor showers.*

Location and etymology

Meteors typically occur in the mesosphere. This is at altitudes between 76 and 100 km from the Earth's surface. The root word of meteor comes from the Greek "meteōros", which means "high in the air".

Mechanism

When an object enters the Earth's atmosphere at a speed of over 20 km per second, it rubs against the atmosphere. Aerodynamic heating produces a streak of light, both from the glowing object as well as the trail of glowing particles that it leaves in its wake.

Meteorite

Incoming objects that are larger than several metres, such as asteroids or comets, can explode in the air. If a meteoroid, comet, asteroid or any piece thereof withstands the wear from its atmospheric entry and impacts the ground, it is called a meteorite.

Frequency

Millions of meteors arrive in Earth's atmosphere daily. Most of them are about the size of a grain of sand. Meteors may occur in showers. These arise when Earth passes through a stream of debris left by a comet. They also arise as "random" or "sporadic" meteors. These are not associated with a specific stream of space debris.

FUN FACT

The observation of many amateur astronomers has allowed us to classify and distinguish between various meteor showers.

Meteor Shower

A meteor shower is "a celestial event in which many meteoroids are seen radiating from one spot in the night sky". Streams of cosmic debris called meteoroids enter Earth's atmosphere at extremely high speeds, causing meteors. The IAU's Task Group on Meteor Shower Nomenclature as well as the IAU's Meteor Data Centre keeps track of meteor shower names.

Dust trail

A meteor shower is caused by an interaction between a planet such as Earth and streams of debris from a comet. Comets can produce debris by water vapour drag. Fred Whipple first demonstrated this in 1951. Each time a comet swings by the Sun in its orbit, some of its ice vaporises and a certain amount of meteoroids are shed. These meteoroids spread out along the entire orbit of the comet to form a meteoroid stream. This stream is also known as a "dust trail". This is distinguished from a comet's dust tail, which is caused by the very small particles that are quickly blown away by solar radiation pressure.

Etymology

Meteor showers are named after the nearest constellation or bright star. A Greek or Roman letter is assigned to the name of the constellation that is close to the radiant position at the peak of the shower. Then, the grammatical declension of the Latin possessive verb form is replaced by "id" or "ids". For example, meteors radiating from near the star delta Aquarii, whose declension is "-i", are called delta Aquariids.

Radiant drift

Meteor shower particles are all travelling in parallel paths at the same velocity. Thus, they all appear to an observer to radiate away from a single point in the sky. This "radiant point" is the effect of perspective.

This apparent "fixed point" slowly moves across the sky during the night. This is due to Earth turning on its axis. It is also the same reason that the stars appear to slowly march across the sky. The radiant also moves slightly from night to night against the background stars due to Earth revolving in its orbit around the Sun. This is termed as the radiant drift.

▲ *A four-hour time lapse photo of the leonids showing the shower from space.*

FUN FACT

Did you know that it is very rare for a meteorite to strike a human being? It is more probable that it will fall into the ocean.

▲ *A meteor shower captured through a telescope.*

Quadrantids

The Quadrantids, or QUA, are a January meteor shower. The Zenithal Hourly Rate (the number of meteors a single observer would see during an hour of peak activity) of this shower is often as high as that of two other reliably rich meteor showers—the Perseids in August and Geminids in December. However, these meteors are not seen as often as meteors in the other two showers. This is because the peak intensity is exceedingly sharp, it sometimes lasts only hours.

Intensity

The meteor rates exceed one-half of their highest value for about eight hours as compared to August Perseids, which do so for two days. Physically, this means that the stream of particles that produces this shower is narrow. Apparently, it has been deriving within the last 500 years from some other orbiting body.

Parent body

Peter Jenniskens tentatively identified the parent body of the Quadrantids in 2003 as the minor planet 2003 EH1. This minor planet may in turn be related to the comet C/1490 Y1. Chinese, Japanese and Korean astronomers observed this some 500 years ago, fitting the timeline.

▼ *A camera trick shot of a meteor shower.*

Radiant point

The radiant point of the Quadrantids is an area inside the constellation Boötes, and not far from the Big Dipper. Astronomers describe it as being located between the end of the handle of the Big Dipper and the quadrilateral of stars that marks the head of Draco the constellation.

Etymology

The name Quadrantids comes from Quadrans Muralis, a former constellation created in 1795 by French astronomer Jérôme Lalande. It is now a part of Boötes. In January 1825, Antonio Brucalassi in Italy reported, "the atmosphere was traversed by a multitude of luminous bodies known by the name of falling stars".

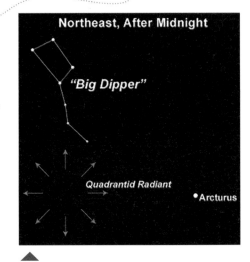

The radiant point of Quadrantid meteor shower, as seen next to the Big Dipper in this diagram.

These meteors appeared to radiate from Quadrans Muralis. In 1839, Adolphe Quetelet of Brussels Observatory, Belgium, and Edward C. Herrick of Connecticut, USA, independently suggested that the Quadrantids are an annual shower.

FUN FACT

When the IAU devised a list of 88 modern constellations in 1922, it did not include the constellation Quadrans Muralis. Therefore, the IAU officially adopted this list in 1930, but this meteor shower still retains the name Quadrantids, based on the original and now-obsolete constellation.

Leonids

The Leonids are a prolific meteor shower. They are associated with the comet Tempel-Tuttle. When this comet debris enters Earth's atmosphere and vaporises we see the Leonid meteor shower. They peak in the month of November. They occur when Earth passes through the debris left by the comet Tempel-Tuttle. This comet orbits the Sun once in about 33 years. At the peak of the Leonid meteor shower you will probably be able to see around 20 meteors.

A camera trick shot of the Leonid meteor shower.

Naming

The Leonids get their name from the location of their radiant, which lies in the constellation Leo. Meteors appear to radiate from that point in the sky. Their proper Greek name should be "Leontids". But, the word was initially formed as a Greek or Latin hybrid because of its structure. It has been in use ever since.

which means it is closer than Jupiter's orbit. The Leonids are a fast-moving stream. They encounter the path of Earth at an average of 72 km per second. Larger Leonids, namely those which are about 10 mm across, have a mass of half a gram. These are known for generating bright meteors.

Mechanism

Earth moves through the meteoroid stream of particles left from the passage of a comet during its revolution around the Sun. This stream comprises solid particles, known as meteoroids, ejected by the comet as its frozen gases evaporate under the heat of the Sun when it is sufficiently close enough,

Scientific background

The meteoroids left by the comet are organised in trails in orbits that are similar to that of the comet. The planets, in particular Jupiter, differentially disturb them. Radiation pressure from the Sun also disturbs them, but to a lesser extent. This is known as the Poynting - Robertson effect as well as the Yarkovsky effect.

peak around 18th November. However, some are spread through several days on either side of the peak and the specific peak changes every year.

A single meteoroid from the Leonid meteor.

Frequency

Old trails are spatially not dense and compose the meteor shower with a few meteors per minute. In case of the Leonids, density tends to

A Leonid meteor as seen at the peak of the shower in 2009.

FUN FACT

An annual Leonid shower may deposit over 12 or 13 tonnes of particles across the entire surface of the planet.

Lyrids

The April Lyrids, or LYR, is a meteor shower that lasts from 16th April to 26th April each year. It is designated as IAU shower number 6. The radiant of this meteor shower is located in the constellation Lyra. It is near the constellation's brightest star, Alpha Lyrae, that is also known as Vega. Their peak is typically around 22nd April each year.

Origin

The source of the shower is particles of dust shed by the long-period comet, C/1861 G1 Thatcher. April Lyrids are the strongest annual meteor shower from the debris of a long-period comet. This is mainly because compared to other intermediate long-period comets, they have a relatively short orbital period of about 415 years. The Lyrids have been observed for the past 2600 years.

Peak and observable meteorites

Meteor showers typically range from 5–20 meteors per hour. Some meteors can be fairly bright. These are known as "Lyrid fireballs". These fireballs cast shadows for a split second and leave behind smoky debris trails that can last for minutes.

Notable Lyrid observations

A strong storm of up to 700 meteors per hour occurred in 1803. This was observed by a journalist based in Richmond, Virginia:

"Shooting stars. This electrical [sic] phenomenon was observed on Wednesday morning last at Richmond and its vicinity, in a manner that alarmed many, and astonished every person that beheld it. From one until three in the morning, those starry meteors seemed to fall from every point in the heavens, in such numbers as to resemble a shower of sky rockets ..."

Another such outburst is the oldest known. The Lyrid shower on 23rd March in 687 BCE was recorded in Zuozhuan. The shower is described as "On day xīn-

Northeast, Late Evening in April

Radiant

Vega

Lyra

The radiant point of the April Lyrid meteor shower, as seen next to Vega in this diagram.

mao of month 4 in the summer (of year 7 of King Zhuang of Lu), at night, fixed stars are invisible and at midnight, the stars dropped down like rain".

The April Lyrid meteor shower.

FUN FACT

Skygazers have been blessed with the sight of as many as 100 Lyrid meteors per hour as happened in America, 1982.

Oort Cloud

The Oort cloud or Öpik–Oort cloud is a spherical cloud of predominantly, icy planetesimals that are believed to surround the Sun at a distance of up to 50,000 AU. It is named after Dutch astronomer Jan Oort and Estonian astronomer Ernst Öpik. It is thought to comprise mainly two regions: a spherical outer Oort cloud and a disc-shaped inner Oort cloud. The inner cloud is also called the Hills cloud.

Origin

The original proto-planetary disc, which came to be formed around the Sun approximately 4.6 billion years ago, could be the origin of the Oort cloud. It is widely accepted that the Oort cloud's objects initially assembled much closer to the Sun. The planets and asteroids were formed due to the same process. However, they were pulled into long elliptical or parabolic orbits due to the gravity of young gaseous giant planets like Jupiter.

Other theories

Recent research by NASA hypothesises that a large number of Oort cloud objects are the product of an exchange of materials between the Sun and its sibling stars. This exchange occurred as they formed and drifted apart. It is currently suggested that most Oort cloud objects were not formed in close proximity to the Sun. NASA simulations on the evolution of the Oort cloud, starting from the beginning of the solar system to the present, suggest that the cloud's mass peaked around 800 million years after its formation. At this point, the pace of accretion and collision slowed, and depletion began to overtake supply.

Hypothesis and discovery

Estonian astronomer Ernst Öpik postulated in 1932 that long-period comets must have originated in an orbiting cloud at the outermost edge of the solar system. Oort independently revived this idea as a means to resolve a paradox about comets. Oort reasoned that a comet could not have formed while in its current orbit. Thus, it must have been held in an outer reservoir for most of its existence.

An artist's rendering of the Oort cloud and Kuiper belt. ▶

A schematic diagram of the structure of the Oort cloud.

Oort's paradox

The orbits of comets are unstable over the course of the solar system's existence. Dynamics dictate that a comet must eventually either collide with the Sun, a planet or be ejected from the solar system by planetary perturbations. Moreover, a comet's volatile composition means that as they repeatedly approach the Sun, radiation gradually boils the volatiles off. This keeps occurring until the comet either splits or develops an insulating crust that prevents further outgassing. This would not be possible in the solar system itself. Thus, comets existing solely in the solar system were paradoxical.

Space Debris

Space debris is the collection of defunct objects in orbit around Earth. It is also popularly known as orbital debris, space junk and space waste. Space debris include spent rocket stages, old satellites and fragments from disintegration, erosion and collisions. As their orbits overlap with new spacecrafts, debris may collide with operational spacecrafts and pose a significant hazard.

Magnitude of the problem

As of 2009, about 19,000 pieces of debris larger than 5 cm are being tracked. There are over 300,000 pieces larger than 1 cm that are estimated to exist below the 2000 km altitude. For a standard of comparison, the International Space Station orbits in the 300–400 km range. Both the 2009 collision and 2007 anti-satellite test events occurred at between 800 and 900 km.

Size and origin

Most space debris are smaller than 1 cm. They include the following:

● dust from solid rocket motors

● products of surface degradation, such as paint flakes

● frozen coolant droplets that are released from RORSAT nuclear-powered satellites

A comparatively big piece of space debris, measuring about 5 cm.

Hazards posed

Impacts of debris particles cause erosive damage in a manner similar to sandblasting. Damage can be reduced by the addition of ballistic shielding to the spacecraft. An example is a "whipple shield", which is used to protect some parts of the International Space Station.

The number of objects in space influence the chance of collision. Thus, there is a critical density where the creation of new debris is theorised to occur faster than the various natural forces that remove them.

An artist's conception of an orbital band of garbage and junk circling Earth. ▶

▲ *Space debris in Earth's orbit.*

Kessler syndrome

Beyond this critical density, a runaway chain reaction may occur, known as the "Kessler syndrome". This would rapidly increase the number of debris objects in orbit. It would, therefore, greatly increase the risk to operate satellites.

Repercussions

The Kessler syndrome would make it difficult to use the polar-orbiting bands. The cost of space missions would increase greatly. Hence, measurement, growth mitigation and removal of debris are activities that are taken seriously within the space industry today.

FUN FACT

Astronomers debate if the critical density has already been reached in certain orbital bands due to the sheer mass of debris present in them.

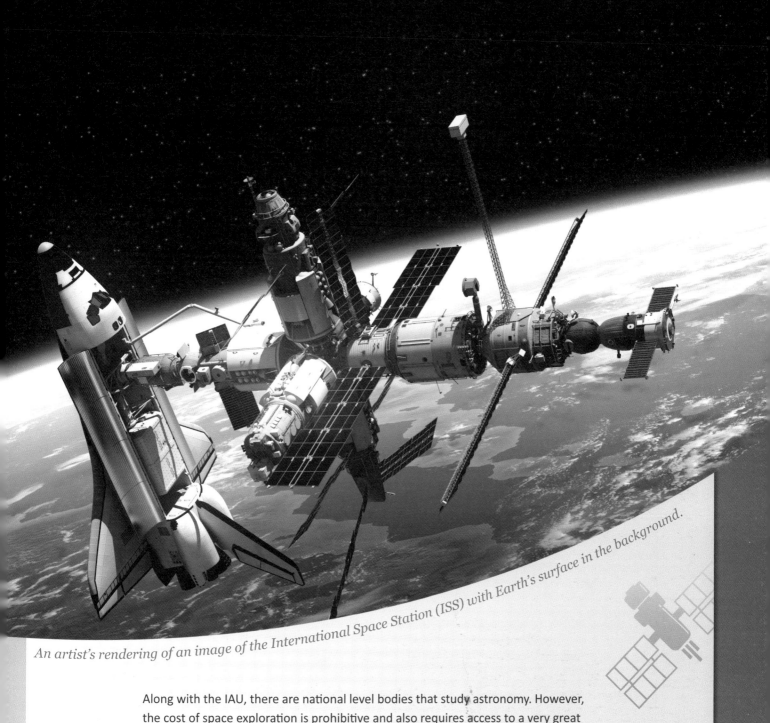

An artist's rendering of an image of the International Space Station (ISS) with Earth's surface in the background.

Along with the IAU, there are national level bodies that study astronomy. However, the cost of space exploration is prohibitive and also requires access to a very great amount of resources. As a result, most governments have designated a governmental agency that co-ordinates and executes space exploration in the country.

Most space agencies lack the funds and resources to conduct all types of space missions. There are multiple private space agencies also interested in spaceflight. Most of these serve as subcontractors for government agencies. However, some, such as Virgin Galactic and SpaceX aim to offer private spaceflight to tourists as well.

NASA

The National Aeronautics and Space Administration (NASA) is a government agency of USA that is responsible for the civilian space programme as well as the aeronautics and aerospace research of USA.

FUN FACT

George Aldrich has worked for NASA for more than 40 years. His job is to smell things to ensure that there are no unpleasant smells on ISS. Interestingly, his nose is also regulated and tested every four months.

Station (ISS). It is also overseeing the development of the Orion multi-purpose crew vehicle, space launch system and commercial crew vehicles. It is responsible for the Launch Services Program (LSP). This programme provides an oversight of launch operations and countdown management for unmanned NASA launches.

Other projects

NASA science is focussed on a better understanding of Earth through the Earth Observing System. It works towards advancing heliophysics through the efforts of the Science Mission Directorate's "Heliophysics Research Program". NASA also focusses on exploring celestial bodies throughout the solar system with the help of advanced robotic missions such as New Horizons.

Environmental impact

Space exploration can affect life and environment on Earth. Some rocket propellants, such as hydrazine, are extremely toxic prior to being oxidised. However, it must be noted that NASA addressed environmental concerns with its cancelled constellation programme in accordance with the National Environmental Policy Act.

History

President Dwight D. Eisenhower established NASA in 1958. It was founded with a distinctly civilian, non-military orientation, encouraging peaceful applications in space science. The

National Aeronautics and Space Act was passed on 29th July, 1958. It disestablished NASA's predecessor, the National Advisory Committee for Aeronautics (NACA). NASA became operational on 1st October, 1958.

◄ *NASA's motto is "for the benefit of all". Depicted here is its seal.*

A part of a rocket designed to travel in space. ▼

Space exploration

NASA has led most of USA's space exploration efforts. Their famous programmes include the Apollo moon-landing missions, the Skylab space station and later the invention of the space shuttle. It is currently supporting the International Space

ISRO

The Indian Space Research Organisation, or ISRO, is the primary space agency of India. ISRO is among the largest government space agencies in the world in terms of both budget and number of missions launched. ISRO's primary objective is to advance space technology and use its applications for national benefit.

▲ *The ISRO logo.*

History

ISRO superseded the erstwhile Indian National Committee for Space Research (INCOSPAR) on establishment in 1969. It, thus, institutionalised space activities in India. India's primary spaceport, the Satish Dhawan Space Centre in Sriharikota is run by ISRO.

Early missions and work

ISRO built India's first satellite, Aryabhata. This was launched by the Soviet Union on 19th April, 1975. Rohini became the first satellite to be placed in orbit by an Indian-made launch vehicle, called the SLV-3 in 1980. Later, ISRO built two more rockets. The one that was used for launching satellites into polar orbits was called the Polar Satellite Launch Vehicle (PSLV). The Geosynchronous Satellite Launch Vehicle (GSLV) could be used to place satellites into geostationary orbits.

▲ *From the public display held at Kanakakunnu Palace at Trivandrum on 29th April, 2015. This is ISROs Space Capsule recovered from the sea.*

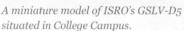

A miniature model of ISRO's GSLV-D5 situated in College Campus.

Recent events and future plans

ISRO sent its first mission to the moon, Chandrayaan-1 on 22nd October, 2008. On 5th November, 2013, ISRO launched its Mars Orbiter Mission. The MoM successfully entered the Mars orbit on 24th September, 2014. Future plans include development of GSLV Mk III to be used for the launch of heavier satellites, development of a reusable launch vehicle, human spaceflight, further lunar exploration, launch of interplanetary probes, a satellite to study the Sun, etc.

FUN FACT

ISRO's Mars Mission team has won the prestigious 2015 Space Pioneer Award in the Science and Engineering category. This is in recognition of achieving the rare feat of entering Mar's orbit in its very first attempt. ISRO is the first Asian space agency to reach the Mars' orbit.

ESA

The European Space Agency or ESA is an intergovernmental organisation dedicated to the exploration of space. Its French-speaking members know it as "Agence spatiale européenne" or ASE. ESA has 20 member states.

European Space Agency

History

ESA was established in 1975 and headquartered in Paris, France. After WWII, Western European scientists realised that solely national projects would not be able to compete with the two main superpowers. In 1958, Edoardo Amaldi and Pierre Auger, who were two prominent members of the Western European scientific community at the time, met to discuss the foundation of a common Western European space agency. This was only months after the Sputnik shock—the surprise launch of the first satellite by the USSR. As of 2014, ESA has a staff of more than 2000 with an annual budget of about €4.28 billion.

Its objective

The treaty establishing the ESA states, "ESA's purpose shall be to provide for and to promote, for exclusively peaceful purposes, co-operation among European States in space research and technology and their space applications, with a view to their being used for scientific purposes and for operational space applications systems".

▲

The ESA Logo. ESA's job is to set up a unified space and related industrial policy. It recommends space objectives to its 22 member states. It is doing its best to integrate national programmes like satellite development into Europe's space programme.

▲ *This image shows the European Space Agency ESA's Headquarters in Paris, France.*

European expendable launch system at the Le Bourget Air show in Paris, France. ▶

Missions and work

ESA's space flight programme includes human spaceflight, mainly through its contribution in the International Space Station programme. It maintains a major spaceport, called the Guiana Space Centre at Kourou, in the French Guiana, and designs launch vehicles. It also works on operations of unmanned exploration missions to other planets and the moon, Earth observation, science and telecommunication.

◀ *European Space Expo in Zagreb, Croatia.*

FUN FACT

ESA's Rosetta mission to explore a comet ended in September 2016.

RFSA

The Russian Federal Space Agency (RFSA) is the government agency that is responsible for the Russian space science programme and general aerospace research. It is commonly called "Roscosmos", which is short for the Russian "Russpace" and abbreviated as FKA and RKA. It was previously the Russian Aviation and Space Agency and commonly known as "Rosaviakosmos".

The Roscosmos logo. Roscosmos is headquartered at Shchepkin Street 42, Moscow.

Major facilities

The headquarter of Roscosmos is located in Moscow. The Main Mission Control space flight operations centre is located in the nearby city of Korolev. The Cosmonauts Training Centre (GCTC) is in Star City. The Launch facilities used by Roscosmos are the Baikonur Cosmodrome in Kazakhstan and Plesetsk Cosmodrome in northern Russia. Baikonur is mostly civilian with most launches occurring there, both manned and unmanned. Military satellites are primarily launched from Plesetsk.

History

The creation of a central agency after the separation of Russia from the Soviet Union was a new development as the Soviet Union did not have a central space bureau. Yuri Koptev became the agency's first director. This agency was later renamed to Roscosmos.

Crisis years

The 1990s saw serious financial problems in Russia because of decreased cash flow. This encouraged them to improvise and seek other financial sources. As a result, they gained a leading role in commercial satellite launches and tourism. Scientific missions, such as interplanetary probes or astronomy missions played a very small role during these years.

However, Roscosmos managed to operate the space station Mir well past

The Soyuz TMA-9 spacecraft launches from the Baikonur Cosmodrome in Kazakhstan 18th September, 2006 carrying a new crew to the International Space Station.

its planned lifespan. It also contributed to the International Space Station and continued to fly additional Soyuz and Progress missions.

Current programme

Some of Roscosmos's future projects are the Soyuz successor, the Prospective Piloted Transport System, scientific robotic missions to one of the Mars moons as well as an increase in lunar orbit research satellites.

Soyuz TMA-13M spacecraft as it arrives at the launch pad by train on Monday, 26th May, 2014, at the Baikonur Cosmodrome in Kazakhstan.

Japan Aerospace Exploration Agency

Japan Aerospace Exploration Agency (JAXA) is Japan's national aerospace working agency. It was established in 2003 and is headquartered in Chofu (Tokyo). It is responsible for technology development, research works, launching of satellites into the orbit, asteroid data, moon exploration and many other advanced missions. The agency's motto is, "Reaching for the skies, exploring space".

▲ *Japan Aerospace Exploration Agency's logo.*

JAXA's projects

- Advanced Land Observation Satellite
- Carbon dioxide monitoring
- Rainfall observation
- GCOM series

JAXA's missions

- Hayabusa: Small body exploration
- Lunar explorations
- Solar sail research

Reaching for the stars

Japan has 10 astronauts. Surprisingly, being a technologically advanced nation it has not developed its own manned spacecraft. They tried to develop a potentially manned space shuttle plane called the HOPE-X project. It was launched by the conventional space launcher H-II and was developed for several years. Unfortunately, the project was postponed. Projects to develop kankoh-maru a single-stage to orbit (SSTO), vertical take-off and landing (VTVL), reusable launch vehicle were started but not adopted.

▲ *A drone developed by JAXA for use during disasters.*

Gen-next technology

JAXA is developing technology for a next-generation supersonic transport. If successful, it could become the commercial replacement for the Concorde. The aim of the supersonic air development project is to create a jet that can carry about 300 passengers at Mach 2. From September to October 2005, aerodynamic testing of a subscale model of the jet was carried out in Australia. How economically successful such a project would be, however, is still not clear, and hence large Japanese aerospace companies like Mitsubishi Heavy Industries have not shown much interest in it.

The science museum at Nagoya that has a rocket on display outside it.

Space Warfare

Space warfare refers to combat that occurs in outer space. This includes ground-to-space warfare, such as attacking satellites from Earth, and space-to-space warfare, such as satellites attacking satellites or spacecrafts attacking each other. Technically, this does not include space-to-ground warfare, that is, where orbital objects directly attack ground, sea or air targets. However, common usage often mixes the two terms.

Existence of satellite weaponry

Currently, some anti-satellite weaponry does exist. This is usually launched from planes or from the Earth's surface. No satellite weaponry currently exists. The People's Republic of China successfully tested a ballistic missile by launching an anti-satellite weapon on 11th January, 2007. On 21st February, 2008, the USA used a SM-3 missile to destroy a satellite USA-193, which is a spy satellite, while it was 247 km above the Pacific Ocean. Japan also uses the SM-3 missile system.

Space weaponry

Space warfare can use a large variety of weapons. Some are currently in existence while others are in the realm of science fiction.

Ballistic Warfare – Systems proposed for ballistic warfare range from measures as simple as ground and space-based anti-missiles to rail guns, space-based lasers, orbital mines and other futuristic weaponry.

An image created to show a missile destroying a satellite in space.

Electronic Warfare – Since spacecrafts and satellites rely very heavily on electronics, these systems are designed to jam, sabotage and outright destroy enemy electronics.

Kinetic bombardment – The energy that a projectile would gain while falling from orbit would make it rival all except the most powerful explosives. Thus, simply dropping objects from orbit is a viable weapons system.

Directed-energy weapons – Weapons like lasers, microwaves, plasma-based weaponry, linear particle accelerators or particle-beam based ammunition all depend upon conveying high energy density to different particles and then using them to target the enemy.

An artists's representation of the future of the USA Space Command in 2020.

FUN FACT

Rail guns and lasers in space, work in most aspects. Currently, the only problem is that the batteries in space aren't big enough to power them.

Space Tourism

Space tourism refers to recreational space travel. It can be either on established government-owned vehicles, such as the Russian Soyuz and the ISS or on the large number of vehicles that are owned by private companies.

The beginning

Space tourism began at the end of the 1990s. It occurred due to a deal between a Russian company MirCorp and an American company Space Adventures Ltd. MirCorp was a private venture responsible for the Russian space station Mir. MirCorp decided to sell a trip to Mir to generate income for the maintenance of the aging space station.

First space tourist

American businessman Dennis Tito was the world's first space tourist on 28th April, 2001. Tito paid $20 million for his flight on the Russian spacecraft Soyuz TM-32. However, before Tito could make his trip, the decision was made to de-orbit Mir. Fortunately, after the intervention of Space Adventures Ltd., the mission was diverted to the ISS and Tito spent seven days on board.

South African computer millionaire Mark Shuttleworth (2002) and American businessman Gregory Olsen (2005) visited the ISS. Iranian-born American entrepreneur Anousheh Ansari became the first female fee-paying space traveller and she visited the ISS in September 2006.

The future of space tourism as digitally rendered by an artist. ▼

Cost of a spaceflight

Most space tourists spend about US $20–30 million for a trip to the ISS. However, in 2007, Space Adventures announced plans to offer a spaceflight around the moon on a Soyuz spacecraft for a fee of US $100 million. As of 2015, Virgin Galactic has seats for tourists at US $200,000 to go into sub-orbital space.

▲ *Dennis Tito, pictured above, is the world's first space tourist.*

FUN FACT

Tito objected to the use of the word "tourist" due to the arduous training required for his mission. Since his flight, the term "spaceflight participant" is used to distinguish commercial space travellers from astronauts.

Space Colonisation

Space colonisation is permanent human habitation off planet Earth. The concept is also called space settlement or extra-terrestrial colonisation. The two most common reasons of its popularity are as follows:

● The survival of human civilisation and the biosphere in case of a planetary-scale disaster.

● The vast resources in space for expansion of human society and the possibilities of development and evolution.

FUN FACT

Many scientists have come out in support of the idea. As a result, science is making rapid advances in self-sustaining technologies that may hold the key to space colonisation.

Space colonies

The building of a space colony presents a set of prohibitive challenges that are both technological and economic in nature. Space settlements would have to provide for all the material needs of hundreds or thousands of humans. This is extremely difficult in an environment that is very hostile to human life.

Space technologies

Technologies, such as controlled ecological life support systems have yet to be developed in a meaningful manner. These would be essential to any long-term settlement. Colonies would have to deal with the issue of how humans would behave and thrive in such places. We have absolutely no data on the long-term effects of space on either our bodies or minds.

The cost of sending anything from the Earth's surface into orbit is colossal – it would cost roughly about US $20,000 per kg. Thus, a space colony would be an extremely expensive project.

▲ *A digitally created image of what space settlements would look like.*

▲ *Goldman Award winner and noted environmentalist Terri Swearingen famously said, "We are living on this planet like we have another one to go to". Her comment highlights the fact that Earth is rapidly running out of resources.*

Planetary Habitability

Planetary habitability is the measure of a planet or a natural satellite's potential to develop and sustain life. Habitability applies to life developed directly on a planet or satellite or that transferred to it from another body.

What makes a planet habitable?

There are many necessary conditions for planetary habitability. These range from the planet itself to the star system in which it resides. They are briefly outlined here.

Stars with a habitable zone

Spectral class – These stars should be sufficiently big to give off the necessary temperature and flare conditions, but small enough to have an adequately long life span to sustain life. There is a shell shaped area around a star, where liquid water can exist and conditions are suitable for life to thrive. This must be stable for evolution.

Low stellar variation – Some stars fluctuate greatly with respect to brightness. This must be sufficiently low so that the planet does not experience any extreme conditions of heat or cold.

High metallicity – The star should contain a sufficient amount of heavier elements (all heavier than Helium and Hydrogen) that will support life.

Requirements for a planet to support life

Mass – This must be adequately large to hold an atmosphere, but small enough to have significant landmasses.

Orbit and rotation – It must have an orbit and rotation that is both moderate and stable. Seasons must occur regularly and not be extreme so that they won't be hostile to life.

Geochemistry – The planet must have sufficient amounts of heavier elements for life to evolve and sustain.

Microenvironments – The environment on the planet should contain micro pockets. The idea is that diversity encourages the evolution of life.

▲ *Moons of certain gas giants satisfy most of these criteria and may be habitable. This is more likely since moons are more numerous than planets.*

▼ *The Atacama Desert is very analogous to Mars' surface. As we can see, it is one of the most lifeless areas on Earth due to a miniscule change in conditions on a cosmic scale.*

Terraforming

Terraforming is the hypothetical process of deliberately altering conditions like temperature, atmosphere, surface topography and even the ecology of a body to create a biosphere similar to the Earth. This may be done to a planet, moon or any other body to make it habitable to Earth-like life. Terraforming literally means "Earth shaping" or creating something like Earth.

An artist's conception of what Mars would look like during various stages of terraforming. ▼

Planetary engineering

The term "terraforming" is rarely used in a general sense. It is used as a synonym for planetary engineering. However, this isn't true. All terraforming is planetary engineering, but the reverse isn't true. The concept of terraforming developed from both science fiction and actual science. Jack Williamson is credited with the idea from a science-fiction story called *Collision Orbit* published in Astounding Science Fiction in 1942. However, it is possible that the concept may pre-date this work.

Possibility of terraforming

Based on experiences with Earth, the environment of a planet can be deliberately altered. However, we're not sure that we can create an unconstrained planetary biosphere on another planet that mimics Earth. Mars is usually considered to be the most likely candidate for terraforming. NASA has even hosted debates on the subject.

Several potential methods of altering the climate of Mars may fall within humanity's technological capabilities. Several studies have been carried out to test the feasibility of altering the temperature and atmosphere of the planet. The timescale involved is long, though possible.

An expensive affair

The terraforming of a planet would be an extremely expensive undertaking with undeterminable results.

The economic resources required to do so are far beyond those that any government or society is willing to allocate. The ethics, logistics, economics, politics and methodology of altering the environment of an extra-terrestrial world are barriers to this concept. However, the speeding up of technology means that this may not be true for long.

▼ *The surface of Mars being explored by an astronaut to contemplate terraforming possibilities.*

Strategic Defence Initiative

US President Ronald Reagan proposed The Strategic Defence Initiative (SDI) on 23rd March, 1983. It aimed to use ground and space-based systems to protect the USA from attack by strategic nuclear ballistic missiles. This was a huge transformation from the regular policy as it focussed on strategic defence rather than on the prior strategic offense doctrine of MAD.

Formation of the SDI and use of space-based weapons

During the early phases of the Cold War, the necessity for anti-ballistic missile systems was realised. Ground-based missiles were found to be too large and cumbersome to be used against Intercontinental Ballistic Missiles, (ICBM) as each missile would have deployed multiple warheads before it could be reliably shot down. However, if the interceptor missiles were placed in orbit, some of them could be positioned over the opposing country at all times. These would fly "downhill" to attack the missiles. Therefore, they had to be much smaller and cheaper as compared to the interceptor which was launched upwards and could target an ICBM in its vulnerable launch phase.

SDI weapons and their designs

The weapons that were considered can be broadly classified as follows:

1. Ground-based programmes
   - Extended Range Interceptor (ERINT)
   - Homing Overlay Experiment (HOE)
   - Exoatmospheric Re-entry-vehicle Interceptor Subsystem (ERIS)

2. Directed-energy weapon (DEW) programmes such as:
   - X-ray laser
   - Chemical laser
   - Neutral Particle Beam
   - Laser and mirror systems, which remained only experimental
   - Hypervelocity Rail Gun in the form of the CHECMATE system

3. Space-based programmes2 such as:
   - Space-Based Interceptor or SBI
   - Brilliant Pebbles

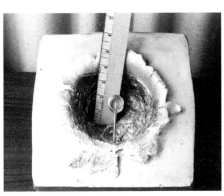

▲ *The SDI tested a Kinetic Energy Weapon by firing a 7 g projectile at an Aluminium test block at 7000 m per second.*

Result of the SDI

Due to the SDI, the US now holds a significant advantage in the field of comprehensive advanced missile defence systems. Under the Bill Clinton administration, the SDI was changed to the Ballistic Missile Defence Organization (BMDO). The current patriot missile defence system would have been impossible without the SDI.

The launching of a payload launch vehicle (PLV), with an exoatmospheric kill vehicle, on 3 December 2001, from the Kwajalein Missile Range at Meck Island. It had to intercept a ballistic missile target over central Pacific Ocean.

FUN FACT

The SDI was very poorly received, both by the masses and scientific community. It was popularly referred to as the Star Wars programme.